Soon

Alba Arikha was born and grew up in Paris. She received an MFA from Columbia University, and now lives in London. She has published a novel, *Muse*, and a short-story collection, *Walking on Ice*. Her previous book, *Major/Minor*, a memoir about growing up in Paris in the 1980s, was shortlisted for the Spears awards and selected among the 'Best Books of 2012' by *The New Yorker*. She is also a singer/songwriter, and has recorded a CD of her songs, *Dans les rues de Paris*.

Praise for *Major/Minor*:

'This is a fiercely honest and compelling account of what it is to grow up in an artistic household, and of the joys and miseries involved in the forging of an independent spirit.'
– John Banville

'An unusually affecting book about the rage and rebellion of a stormy adolescence . . . I read it straight through, unable to stop.' – Paul Auster

'The ability to let prose ease into poetry, as Arikha does here, is rare.' – Natasha Lehrer, *Times Literary Supplement*

'Evoked with tactile sensitivity and poetic flair, Alba Arikha's childhood is also freighted by history . . . Memoir here becomes the sister to the best rite of passage fiction.'
– Lisa Appignanesi

also by Alba Arikha

FICTION

Muse
Walking on Ice

MEMOIR

Major / Minor

Alba Arikha

Soon

An edited version of *Soon* was performed as an opera, with music by Tom Smail, at the Riverside Studios, London, in August 2013.

First published in 2013
by CB editions
146 Percy Road London W12 9QL
www.cbeditions.com

Printed in England by Blissetts, London W3 8DH

ISBN 978-0-9573266-8-2

For Tom

Contents

Stained

I wish my brother were dead. That's what I wish
the woman said to her husband, a short man with round
glasses and a pale face that kept turning towards the train
window
when she wasn't speaking.
She said it again, DEAD, do you hear, DEAD would be
better than what he's putting us through now.
The man shook his head sadly and slowly
just to show her that he had heard
as if that still mattered
so many years of trying to understand
why
when
how
or maybe he knew
that it was no longer about understanding
but accepting that nothing
was the same
she was stained
like a piece of clothing
only recognisable by certain traits
once loved
now where?
Too tired to search
but still sometimes
only sometimes
he thought he had found her again
so for those sometimes
he stayed

though most of him was gone
lonely but she didn't know
didn't see
a drained man with no colour
no drive
no self left
his own fault for being so weak someone had said
a friend once
no longer.
He wanted to be still but she wouldn't let him
because she needed to be heard
always
and needed to speak
always
and needed to be loved
always
in case she found herself alone
never
except at night when she slept after drinking
too many glasses of wine
from a bottle of Bordeaux she would leave on the wooden
kitchen table
the one they had bought in France many summers ago
in an antique shop in the Loire valley
when things were still fresh between them
and everything about her was new
her eyes
the smell of her hair
her lips
the way her voice became raspy when she laughed.

I looked at the husband
at his face
at the way she spoke to him

and stuck her long vermilion nails out
like hooks
and how he recoiled
shoulders hunched
head lowered
as she hissed
again
about the brother and his mental disorder
about her husband and how he just sat there
about things I couldn't hear
words spinning inside her painted lips
like a wheel.
Then she smiled
gently
as if nothing had happened
as if everything was normal
she smiled and sipped on a cup of tea then
STOP
the train screeched
suddenly
an hour outside of Paris
pale yellow flatlands and raindrops falling
tentatively on the window
facing a forgotten road
and a forlorn building
with rusty balconies
and walls grey
like dry clay.
Everything was quiet now
as she was
looking at a French book then raising
her eyes
seeing me seeing her
seeing inside her

inside the husband
she now despised though
after all those years
she couldn't remember
why.

Ten years one day

Train brought to a standstill as
a man's voice comes onto the loudspeaker –
We apologise for this technical problem, we're dealing
with it and will keep you updated.
Updated.
Hours maybe
or minutes
possibly
stuck here on the train
with the couple
both reading now
each holding a thick book
whose title is hidden by their fingers.
'Arrête!'
A child cries out
no one seems to look up
but me
as another child answers back and they bicker in French
while their mother stands up and
starts to pace and speak too loudly on her mobile phone
which has been ringing continuously
'Tu comprends Mathilde, cette salope'
You understand Mathilde, that bitch
she says
while her children continue to bicker
no matter that their mother curses in front of them
she often does that
they will say if pressed
for details.

A steward comes by with a trolley and some tea
which he pours carefully into a little cup
'Enjoy'
he smiles
big word
for such a small offering.
He has white teeth and kind eyes
he comes from East Africa
I would guess
but will not ask him
in case it starts a conversation I'd rather have
later
maybe
if the train
is still here
not there
not in the street I'm walking on
where the air smells of spring
on the rue Jacques-Callot where I've stopped for a coffee
in that same café I used to sit in
twenty-five years ago
when my makeup was too heavy and my expectations
too small though they felt so big
then.
The waiter is the same man I knew
beady eyes, sour face
reluctant smile
I remind him
of that time
because I want him to remember
to smile
to say 'Oh yes, of course'
to show him my loyalty
to prove that my ties

are forever forged
in the pavements of the city
I left
long ago.
'I was eighteen, I came here a lot.'
'So did many others'
he mumbles because for him
time is an irrelevant
slew of faces
some of which he warmed to
some of which he ignored.
I was young here once
with the same smell in the air and the same
feeling of freedom
of wild expectations
of life unfolding like a velvet promise
of possibilities.
I kissed a boy on a chair
there
at the table underneath the white awning
he had red hair, brown eyes
and a warm tongue
we lingered and drank *kirs royals* until closing time
when we were asked to leave
by the same waiter
who still doesn't remember
when I ask him.
Why would he, I realise
this is all about me, not him
my significant moment
his routine
his every day
melded into one blur
ten years one day

all the same
like it was with X
days turned into months into years
of odium
sharp then dull
because normality had ceased to exist
as I knew it when we first met
I had been warned
but didn't pay heed
because I was young
and wanted to be
happy.
I didn't know
that words could hurt more
than blows
aimed like gunshots
'you you you you you you'
X
piercing deeply
beyond the skin
into a place
I hadn't known existed
a cold, cavernous labyrinth
where shards of despair gather like ants
and harden like molten rock.
Pain is pointy
like an arrow
I lived with its nib
scraping relentlessly
against my soul sinking
in quicksand
until the movers arrived
one June afternoon
and I left

for a place
streaked with sun
together with my children
and my belongings
in sealed cardboard boxes.

Cannons hidden among flowers

for S.K.

Frédéric Chopin walks into the carriage
and sits down in the empty seat
beside me.
'But you died in 1849'
I gasp
'I did,' he whispers
in case someone might overhear him
or see him
like I do.
His music is the ghost
I have forever chased
forever loved
I will not tell him
as he must know
otherwise
why would he be here?
His power is concealed
within his frailty, his pale skin
and sunken eyes.
'I've been ill ever since I was a child'
he tells me.
His voice is muffled
a wisp of a man
with dapper clothes
black cravat wound around his neck
spotless white gloves on his hands.
He was Fryderyk in Poland
his birth house
had linden trees

in the garden.
He arrived as
Frédéric in Paris
a prodigy from Warsaw
twenty years old
clutching a silver goblet
of Polish soil
leaving
lost loves
behind
replaced by new loves
in Paris
where music flowed from his
slender fingers
melodic kernels
cosmic *rubatos*
working their spell on all
who heard him improvise
late at night
in those Parisian salons with
heavy brocade curtains
and Gobelins tapestries
hanging among colourful still-lifes
and women swooning over him
in their crinoline skirts
and puffy sleeves.
'*Cannons hidden among flowers*'
said Robert Schumann
about Frédéric
even when the white keys
would drip red
from his coughed blood.
Those were the good years
he says

though his health was poor
menacing
like impending thunder
'I knew that I would die
young, as I did
too young
maybe.'
Never mind
posterity's conjecture
– demanding
calculating
spoiled –
'a moral vampire'
greatness was his alibi
genius some said
so does it all matter
in the end?

Yes, I can see that George
might have tired of him
there in Valldemossa
where they lived
a Carthusian monastery
in the Spanish mountain range
no monks left
all gone
only one man
an old drunken servant
shuffling
through the cloisters
clutching
an ancient bell
calling the monks
by their names.

Slivers of morning sun
became blue shadows
by afternoon,
night shadows too
dancing nightmares
'I saw things,' he says
laudanum kept him
company
even during the day
when he played
on an old piano,
sadness transformed
into preludes
which echoed
the incessant rain
outside.
Aurore had been her name
Aurore for dawn
before she became George,
the one he came to love
she who smoked cigars
and wore trousers
and was the toast of the town –
would she have been softer
as Aurore
I wonder
her ardour faded
from lover
to 'mother'
she was the man
he the frail woman
always sickly
never happy
she called him 'my little cadaver'

then wrote a book
– he became Prince Karol
to her Lucrezia Floriani –
did she know how great he was?

I tell him
that the monastery in Valldemossa
has become
a lucrative tourist destination
a piano
– passed off as his –
the cell he had slept in
the blue mountains
he had watched from his window
the kitchen he had eaten in
the cloisters
the old servant had
shuffled through
with his bell.

Somewhere
I tell him
inside one of the cold rooms
someone had also discovered
a strand of his hair.

He turns and looks at me
my apparition
my hero
but instead of a smile
there is a sneer
an ugly rictus forming
on his soft features
that tells of

something dark
and fractured
something that began
behind the shutters
of that house
with the linden trees,
something I will never know
because
he is gone
no trace
that we have ever spoken
no trace
that he has ever been.

I would like
to have
told him
that at his death
the Polish soil he had carried
as a young man
had been strewn
on his coffin
and his heart
taken back to Poland
and sealed inside a church pillar
by his sister
who had never stopped
loving him.

Soon

I

He drinks milk
no more
my son
not
like he used to
when his pure
grey gaze was new
and fresh
like open air
a gaze now firm
like his grown feet,
his words
pithy, eager
earnest sometimes,
but he is after all
standing on the doorstep
of manhood not quite
inside yet
though nearly there.

Soon
he will be far, further
than when I left him
in that place
when You tied
his first tie
and my finger brushed against

the coarse fabric
of his shiny black uniform
and I touched
his cheek
to say goodbye.
He was young then
his voice just breaking
his bed untidy
until his return
so that I could pretend
that he was still there
upstairs
in his bedroom
and would be
coming down
anytime

Soon.

II

There are memories
missing
of his smallness.
I forage for them
in the murky coves
of my mind
but can only retrieve
bits of them
and every one of them,
every bit
hurts
not because the moment is gone

but because everything
about that time
still stings.

Damage
is a box
I have
briefly held,
but I don't like
its cruddy
green colour
nor the way
it digs
its insidious
claws against
the grain
of my vain
skin.

We shared a kingdom
my son and then
my daughter
of play and fantasy
of French tales
and songs
of Pokémon cards
and patisseries
bought at the bakery
on Harrington Road
which smelled
of warm bread
and hot chocolate
and where a saleslady
with a white apron

knew their names
for a while.

Then the kingdom
was invaded
by hostile forces
so we started over
in that place
streaked with sun
where what
was lost
had to be reconquered
though they missed
the old kingdom
they whispered
they wanted it back.
So I enfolded
my children
into the nub
of my peace
and I told them this:
that I would
cup the breeze
in my hands and lift
the sky and lift
the rain and search
for hidden pockets
of gold-leafed
drops
to sprinkle
the earth
with liquid
bloom.

When?
they asked.

Soon.

The sea, I said

I

There is a woman. Sitting by the door. It slides loudly. She wears a blue jumper. A beaded necklace. She looks out the window. Her features look fragile. She's thinking of her husband. He's away on business. She doesn't trust him. She crosses her arms. The train doesn't move. She turns her head towards me.
I know her. I've seen her before. At a party in Chelsea. The waiters were Portugese. Everyone was rich. Everything was expensive. Even the noise. Even the smells. Air clogged with entitlement. She wore a long black dress. She laughed loudly. Her legs were long. You found her pretty. Some music came on. She swung her hips. So did the others. Let's leave, you said. A man came towards us. He was drunk. He spoke of birds. You enjoyed him. We stayed. You mentioned buzzards. Then marshes.
The sea, I said. No one heard.
We went home.
Your hand was warm.

II

I have bought
36 houses
most of them
in France
but some in Greece

and a few
more remote ones
in the Italian Apennines.
I have bought
land in the Cevennes
wrecks in the Limousin
with former piggeries
and disused bread ovens
and transformed Provençal
shacks into manors
and swum in my own
Ardèche river
and ambled on the
cobblestones
of a medieval village
where the same
hunched man
serves me milk
in the shop
with the
sylvan smell
and the creaky door
he never bothered
to repair.

House-porn
you say and smile
when I tell you
of my latest
acquisition.
I crave my
personal soil
and you nod
in sympathy

too sensible
to share
my endorphine releasing
fantasies.

I see
the sea
even here on the train
still standing
not moving
– how long? –
rain beating
obstinately
against the window.

Dim light outside,
it could be morning
or afternoon
the train manager
delivers a message
in a grinding voice
we will keep you
informed.

The couple in front of me
are sleeping now
her mouth
open
her head
resting softly
on his shoulder.
If I didn't know
I would say
they were
at peace.

III

I see
the sea
its silver shadow
a mystic glitter
to undulate in
and dream of
(*ladies and gentlemen*
we apologise for the delay)
a Greek place
at the tip of time
where the straits of
the Dardanelles
flow into
the sea
of Marmara.

You remember
that summer
in Pelion
we sat outside
on the terrace
underneath the
dripping bougainvillea
and watched
the sun
plunge hot
red
into the cobalt
blue
and drank
white wine
while the Meltemi

wailed
like a wounded animal.

On a cobbled mule path
we passed a shepherd
with a face
carved from stone,
a flock of
sheep treading
behind him
like docile children
an old dog
limping
by their side.

At dusk
we heard
the call
of the shepherd
echoing through
the mountain
wilds.

Sprezzatura

I'm not happy with my husband
anymore
says Sophie
the woman
with the beaded necklace
who is now standing
by my side
with her dark hair
green eyes
and puckered skin
like a cracked
Renaissance portrait,
her hand resting
on the seat cover
dark shadows
under her eyes,
hollow pockets
of disquietude.

She has recognised me and
engages in small talk
before she moves
too quickly
into more intimate territory
perhaps because
she needs to speak
rather than be heard
'He says, I want, he doesn't, we will'

she repeats
never mind that I don't
want to listen
this isn't about me
but her
I recognise
the tone
of distress
of words bumping
into each other
incoherently
because distress
is an urgency
that cannot
be expressed
steadily
at least not
in her case
and nor was it
in mine
when I was
there
many years
back
standing in
that same place
she is
in now.

My husband
won't let me leave him
she tells me
as she sits down
next to me

uninvited.
He loves me
still
he says
he wants to make
this work
he says
he doesn't want
the children
to suffer.

So I will have
to leave one day
or one night
without any warning
because it is
a fairy tale
gone sour
although
it didn't have to
end that way
but he chose
this path
and now
it's doomed.

But is it
really? I ask
even though
I don't really want
to know
the answer,
as I don't wish
to revisit that

viperous vale
of stifled senses
and searing
invective
I left it
long ago and
she's standing there
now
in the beginnings of it,
right before
civility
loses its balance
and tips
into darkness.
I can see it
all over again
I wish she'd say
no more
but she does
and fiddles
with her necklace
and asks me
about You
and us
and money –
no problems there
she says, I'm lucky –
so I don't respond
because
I'm not
lucky there
though that hasn't
stopped me
from living

as I wish to.
I used to excel
at the art of
female
sprezzatura
she says to me
in a perfect
Italian accent
I could always
pretend that everything
was effortless
and easy
though now
I will no longer
pretend
even though
my husband still does
and still thinks
I don't know
about the affairs
and the woman
who fell in love
with him
last summer,
she wore a
white dress
and a gold medallion
around her neck
and I knew
that she would love him
but he always
denied it
even though
she scattered

clues
like leaves
because she
wanted me
to know
YOUSEE
yousee
yousee
you
you
You
and your
blue eyes
dancing
in our kitchen
with the dog
lying in
a puddle
of sunshine
while
you wash
the dishes
and we laugh
and listen
to Radio 4
together.

Speaking to dragonflies

The boy a few seats
ahead of me
is becoming fractious
and his mother raises
her voice and says
'Behave Timmy or else'
but Timmy or else
doesn't want to behave
because what he
was saying before
was not bad
just true
and why does his mother
always get so angry
when he says things
she doesn't understand?
The mother stands up
now I can see half
of her face
she reaches for
a small bag
in the luggage rack
above,
her hair
is untidy
there are patches of sweat
underneath her arms
her eyes
are worried

they dart quickly
across the carriage
like small bullets
then back to her son
who says
that he could
speak to dragonflies
in his other life
(you're such
a liar, says his sister)
he was sure of it
he lived in a cave
with dragonflies
who were his friends
and where everyone
was nice and
understood each other.

His mother
sits down again
and she laughs raucously
shades of pain
gathered underneath
that leak
like drops
from a cracked ceiling.
She tells
Timmy to stop
his nonsense talk
about dragonflies
they've already
established
that one cannot
speak to dragonflies

and what nonsense
is this about
homes not being
nice when he,
Timmy,
is such
a *lucky lucky*
boy, he has
to count his blessings
that he has
such a lovely house
and that his mother
has devoted her life
to him and his sister
how dare he invent
such things
she says,
her voice rising
as someone's phone
begins to ring
and the train manager
makes another announcement
no one can hear
because Timmy has started to shout
about wanting to see
his father and
liking him
better
and liking dragonflies
better than his mother –
he's incoherent now
and his sister screams
'Shut up!' several times.
A few passengers

turn their heads
towards the mother
and give her
and her children
disapproving
glances
so she becomes silent
and says
nothing more
though Timmy
does
then he too
stops because a
strident sound
like a broken microphone
can be heard
through the
intercom system
and we all
cover our ears
with our hands
until it stops.
The carriage
feels hot
and sticky now
and a smell of freshener
wafts unpleasantly
from the washrooms.
The woman
in front of me
starts complaining
about the smell
and the heat
and the noise

and the woman
and her awful son
and the awful weather
and this awful train
and this awful service.
Her husband looks at her
and says, 'Polly,
we're stuck
there's nowhere for us
to go'
so she has a name now
Polly –
though when I look
at her dour face
I see
a different name
something guttural
and Northern
like a cold
black wind.

White light

for G.C.

I remember the coldness
of the blue tiles underneath
my bare feet
in the Jerusalem house
filled with books
on that street
with eucalyptus trees
where we stayed
for a while
with the poet
who smoked
too much
and coughed
always
and shouted
sometimes
at his wife
who took it all
in her stride.
The poet
I was told
had translated
Shakespeare
into Hebrew
and was a great writer
but as a child
I didn't know
why greatness
should be relevant

to the man
who ate and
smoked unfiltered cigarettes
and told jokes
and made my mother
laugh
because that was
what mattered
to me
though not
to my father
the painter
who valued
the mind more
than the
everyday.

I remember
the smell of pine
on the tarmac
of Ben Gurion airport
'How beautiful'
my father would say
of his beloved city
2400 feet
above sea level
we would climb
an open road
through the morning fog
through the valley of cedars
and the cleft hills shaped
like hunchbacks
and the white
dusty rock

which my father called
his other home
the one
whose presence
we were always
reminded of
and never allowed
to forget –
'this is the
stone I love
best' –
though the
blinding light
he said
was too harsh
for painting.

Today my father
is gone
and that same
open road
has been divided
by a wall
and though the smells
are the same
and the rock
and the light are still
as white
and the language
still feels
like a familiar
stranger
it no longer sits
as comfortably

inside me
as it did
then.

There is a woman
in our garden
carrying a basket
of folded laundry
she leaves it for my mother
on the doorstep
of the house
we moved into
later on
in another dusty
Jerusalem street
with a tall
black iron gate
and a Romanian housekeeper
who never smiled
and two old labradors
who slept
most of the day.
I fell in love
there
in that house
my first love
so perhaps this is why
I remember it all
so vividly
and I wonder
looking at Polly
if her first love
is still vivid
or if it has

become something
she has buried
inside a closet
together with
all those other
accrued memories
she doesn't want
to sift through
for fear that
they will all
come tumbling
down.

Milk teeth

I

With You
I speak an atmosphere
as I do with my children
as I did with my father
and the world
he belonged to
which I can no longer
recapture
though it has left
its residue
in my identity
creating the outline
of a shadow
I have kneaded
into my own
shadings
with one pigment only
blue 29
aquamarine
and lapis lazuli
infused
in small drops
inside our rootless
blood stream.

What would he say to me
today

my father
I often wonder
I think of him
always
so much to ask him
yet
so much he would have liked
to know
about the shape
of our lives
and how his gene pool
has produced more children
with his eyes
and the drip
of his verve
everywhere
inside us
guiding us
to different places
with unexpected outcomes
some of which
he may not have
necessarily understood
but would have
ultimately
approved of
or at least that's what we all
need to think
or do we
still.

I had time
to say goodbye
before he died

his voice was small
and he had been
my thunder
now no more
it was the day
after his birthday
our home was filled
with flowers from the day
before
and the smell
lingered
for days
even when we returned
from the morgue
where a man
opened a door for us
and told us to enter
a room where my father lay
on a trolley
his face shiny
and chalk white
his hands folded
in stern black
leather gloves
'He looks like an emperor'
my mother said
but I couldn't see an emperor
only a wax imitation
of the man I had known
and no longer recognised
and wished I had never seen
that way.

Three years since he died
his grave bears his name
in grey letters
'artist' it says
the air where
he lies speaks
in breaths
last time I stood there
someone had left a small
circle of pebbles
in the shape of a heart
I shall go and visit
him
I shall.

II

I never took her
to Legoland
as I had promised
and never cooked him
my own vegetable soup
though he asked
many times
then
no more.

I tried
to honour all
my other promises
rarely faltering
though when I did
guilt was unremitting

suspended
like a crate
in mid-air
until it
eventually
made its
descent
towards a
more jagged
ground.

III

I will always be
Maman
but not always Mother
as I am now
needed, wanted
her love
still fresh
her limbs
still growing
her tastes
changing
into what
she will become
later
her candour
still pure
though her moods
more sultry
sprouting their own
buds and leaves and colours –

furious red
feisty orange
tender blue –
no more pinks
or Barbies
or nursery rhymes
what was once loved has been
replaced by a new fad
which is embraced
with the same vigour
as the previous one
and shall continue to be
until she finds
her own way
without me.

There are boxes
of her old clothes
gathering dust
inside a cupboard
divided into sizes –
here are the twos
and the fours
and the sixes
small shoes
and frilly dresses
here is the skirt
she wore
at a birthday party
in Gloucester Road
and here is
a milk tooth
forgotten in its pocket,
small with dried

blood stains
on the enamel.
I remember her smile
and the pale yellow shirt
and the hair clips in her hair
she wore when You first met
and You drew a house together
sitting on an oriental cushion
I had bought
on the Portobello Road
and the sun was shining
through the open window
with the view of the rooftops
and I could tell then
that she would
love You
in time.

No matter what

A man with a white shirt
is standing by Sophie's seat
he is tall with brown hair
and he is speaking
loudly enough for me to hear
his French accent and one or two
allusions to what he 'inadvertently'
heard her say to me before
about her husband and wanting to
leave him but him not letting her,
'That must be so hard,' he says
in false commiseration which
she accepts instead
of being taken aback
by his indiscretion
though perhaps indiscretion is
what she's looking for as
she asks him to sit down besides her
which he does all too happily,
a conventionally
handsome man
with long fingers
and bushy eyebrows.

The man tells her
about a fruit shop
on the Harrow Road
where an old Afghan man
with blue eyes

and dark skin
sells kumquats
on Saturdays only
he was a regular, the man says
and often spoke to the old Afghan
about fruit and seasons
and the country
he had never gone back
to visit
until now as
his cousin had bought the old man
a ticket and he was finally
going home to a village
in the Hindu Kush mountains
on the Pakistani border.

That morning, on his way to the station
the man had stopped by the shop
to wish him a good trip
but the shop was closed down
because the old Afghan
had died
in his sleep.
'I've been thinking about him all morning'
the man says
and Sophie smiles softly
at him and I can see
in her smile and the sparkle in her eyes
that she will do whatever he asks of her
because she wants him
as he wants her
though he will take
his time with this
beautiful woman

too good to be true
though complicated
he noticed that she let
some telling words
slip
out of her net
into his palm
and thirsty long fingers
it is now a matter of what
he chooses to do
with her words
and how long
before his palm
becomes restless.

I was there
a few years ago
where Sophie is now,
leaving one life
for another
stepping into
the forgotten territory
of unwelcomed encounters
and tentative
possibilities
where freedom
is a wide
open window
wind flowing softly
like iridescent velvet
against parched
skin.

I see the
man lean
towards Sophie
'My name is Fabien'
her skin is flushed now
her voice is modulating
for him
and I know
that soon after
she returns to London
no matter what does
or doesn't happen
with this man
she will have left
her husband
for good
and the cockpit
of their unity
will stall
and sink
down and
away.

One step away

Polly is furious –
FURIOUS –
she says to her husband
who is resting with
his head tilted
backwards,
Teddy, this is absolutely
OUTRAGEOUS
she hisses, though I cannot hear
her other words
muffled like a gloved hand
underneath her
ranting diatribe,
so she elbows him
'Teddy, Teddy'
until she gets a
modicum of an answer,
he feels unwell
he says
weak, hot, no good
'So take a pill
for god's sake Teddy'
she says, handing over
a packet of paracetamol
which he touches
feebly, limply
no, not that
he says so she retreats
back to her muffled

venting
sitting so near to me
though so far away
in spirit
as are many
but not all
strangers in my life
those with whom
I cross paths
every day
in shops
on the street
on the bus
on the tube
on the pavement
one step away
ten worlds
apart
like my neighbour
with whom I exchange a few words
sometimes
though I find
that we share
little
except for the white wall
between our Victorian
houses.

The steward with the
kind eyes returns
with some more tea
and apologises for the delay
most unusual, he says
and most distressing

but then again
no system
is perfect
he adds
perhaps referring to his
country, Eritrea
which he left
seven years before
he says with a faint
trace of emotion I mistake
for nostalgia
quickly refuted
when he tells me –
pouring the hot tea
into a small
white cup –
that his nostalgia has been
buried in the
African sand
and the windowless cells
where people
disappear
like the wind
like his father
whom he never saw again
incommunicado
so he escaped
with his mother
and sister
to Libya
through the Sahara
and on
into England
where he now lives

and takes night classes
so that he can become
an engineer
someday.

One step away
five worlds
apart
no intractable void there
I admire
his bravura
and his tenacity
speaks to me
as does
his dignity
untarnished
by the debris of his past
though perhaps
a sliver of grief remains
shaped
like a crescent moon
buried
inside the lining
of an old coat
pocket.

Pavo Pani Pana

The air conditioning system on the train
has broken down
and I can feel the heat
billowing
across the carriage
like a cloud of smoke
sticky like
thick honey
against my
sweaty flesh
and all those
faces around me,
composed at departure
now creased
like pillows.

'I need to stretch my legs'
says Sophie
to Fabien
who follows her
somewhere else
somewhere cooler
quieter
where they might
drink a cup of tea
and get to know each other
better
their desire enfolded
underneath

coated words
and bashful
body language.

Prolonged immobility
produces unrest
a puddle of
charcoal tar
which I could touch
with my finger
if I had
such powers,
fading now as I
sink into
a broken sleep
and dream
a protean
palette of colours
green blue
with a splash of
yellow
or is it
white
images floating like
a rowing boat
then stopping
as a cloaked
figure appears
again
always the same sinister
presence
I have yet
to identify
lurking in the penumbra

somewhere inside
my house
this is when I wake
and scream
and find You
holding me
'I'm here, my love'
though not this time
not here
not You
but someone else
is peering, speaking to me
dream interrupted
by a man
with a pockmarked face
and rancid breath
who stands over me
his hand resting
too casually
on my seat
nearly touching
my hair
'Hello hello I'm speaking
to you how are you'
he has a Mancunian
accent I think
(You would know
You always do)
go away I feel like saying
to the man
though I wish
it could be that easy.

I'm sure we've met before,
where do you live?
he asks
again
as if
I were going to answer
a complete stranger
as if
he had the right to stand there
and badger me with
more questions
which he does –
what is your name
where do you come from
what do you do –
perhaps he is mad I wonder
so I reply
carefully
that I need
to rest and that I don't
remember ever meeting him
so he smiles at me
and hisses
Of course you would say that
but don't think I believe you, don't
you think it, you know and I know
that we met before
at the house of Sammy Parson
– who? –
yes Sammy, the drummer
from Poole
Poole swimming
in pools with pills
I forgot

my pills
maybe my brother
hid them
Pavo Pavi Pana
that's what he used to say
though never explained
what it meant
never
he wore shorts
and a small cap
and knees scraped
from climbing
too many trees
but he's dead
two years now
Pavo Pavi Pana
yes, must go now
au revoir au revoir
you pretty thing
but he doesn't leave
so my blood
freezes
because yes
he is mad
and madness frightens me
especially now
trapped in
this heated space
here
somewhere in the outskirts
of Paris
I musn't answer
I must ignore him
ask for help

yes
now
though
no
he seems
to pause
and closes
his eyes
then opens them
and grins
at the ceiling
and squeezes his knuckles
together
as if in a
hard prayer –
then walks away
his knuckles
still squeezed
together –
I'm calling security
says Polly
loudly
looking at me –
no need to but thank you
I reply
he's gone and
he's harmless
so she shrugs
and fiddles with a mint wrapper
and places the sweet
in her mouth
while Teddy stares
out of the window
his gaze empty

too late really
he knows, doesn't he
that the fine-toothed lines
combing his face
bear the stamp
of pain, stealthy clues
which he hasn't
picked up
in time.

Modi the cursed

There is a reproduction
of a painting
on the cover of a book
Sophie left behind
on her empty seat
a woman with an oblong face
and languorous blue eyes
the artist's lover perhaps
Jeanne Héburtene
so young so beautiful
says Modigliani
standing in front of
53 Boulevard de Montparnasse
where he lives
with an English poet
Beatrice
they met at the terrace of the
Rotonde café
that summer of 1917
where he was wandering
from table to table
his paintings rolled up
in newspaper –
'I am Modigliani! Jew!
Give me a drink and
the work can be yours!'
his hair was black and curly
his eyes green
his profile Greek

irresistible
Beatrice said
and succumbed
like many others
before her.
'They call me
Modi'
he laughs
'French for cursed
because I am' –
everything about Modi
is rushed
his appearance
his thoughts
the way he speaks –
haltingly, as if every minute
might be his last –
'You see
I cannot tell the others
no one
though I can tell you
as you are not really here
are you
so let me say then
that sweeps of lassitude
and nocturnal spasms
befall me increasingly
though Beatrice doesn't know
my English fairy
dissolute
by default
my presence is a malediction
she says
though she loves it

secretly
but will never plunge
as deeply as I have
because she cares
about appearances
more than I do
and cares about life
more than I do
because all that matters
to me
is to paint
and paint
and paint
never mind that my teeth
are falling out
so Vive l'opium!
my new friend
as is hashish
and its weaker cousin
anything to detract
from the truth
that I am a fucked-up
vagabond
but women give me
such pleasure
when I appear
they all go weak
at the knees don't they
so why don't you sit
for me, nice name
Alba
with your curly hair
and green eyes
why don't you sit here'

he says, pointing to
a wooden stool covered
in splashes of white
– so he begins
to paint me
in his studio
first the nose
then the eyes
the mouth
the face
with the smell of turpentine
and watercolour
smudges
on the floor
he wears a dark waistcoat
and a white
shirt rolled up
at the sleeves
and his sleepy eyes
gaze at me
I can see why
they all fall for him
I might have too
if I could
in another life
or is this
the other life
as I sit now
on his
wooden stool
where a few days later
he will have completed his portrait
and shows me how
the bristle of his brush

has painted my neck
an elongated yellow,
my eyebrows
an arched black
my eyes slanted
my nose
narrow
my hair
auburn
'Come for a drink with me
afterwards'
he says
'Max Jacob
is waiting
with Zadkine
the painter
and probably a few more
of us
dissolute types'
he says, lightly
as if proud
of the stigma
he has inflicted
upon himself
unaware that he is
tolerated but not always
welcomed
in certain places
though whether he cares
or not
is debatable
and perhaps irrevelant
he would argue
though

the wayward dart
of recklessness
is never irrelevant.

When the painting is finished
I follow him to the Rotonde
where I am introduced to Max Jacob
the poet, his friend
who shakes my hand
and offers me a drink
just as Sophie
and the man walk back
to their seats
brimming
with expectancy
as a faint
streak of sun
inches forward
in the anthracite
sky, shining its rays
on the window
of the train
which after sixty minutes
has finally begun
to move again
leaving behind
the forgotten road
and the forlorn buidling
from where
moments before
an old woman came out
wearing a rain bonnet
and carrying
a brown paper bag.

Coda

In twenty minutes we shall be arriving at Paris-Gare du Nord
announces the train manager, apologising yet again
for the terrible inconvenience
caused by a technical problem
and offering us free vouchers
which we can redeem anytime in the next six months –
'Who knows where we'll be then,' Polly snarls
her skin hard like old leather
'Who knows if our house will still be standing,
if my cursed brother will still be alive
if you and I, Teddy, will still be part
of this godforsaken world'
'Why shouldn't we be,' says Teddy
looking as white as a sheet
which Polly comments on
his whiteness
his meekness
his uselessness
his sweaty hands
and sad eyes
always ill
always sad never happy
she says
'And what about you, Polly, what about you
aren't you the sad one?'
he asks in a wisp of a voice
thin like bobbin thread
about to break apart any moment now
so she laughs, the croaky laugh

of someone who has smoked all her life
Chesterfield unfiltered, never before midday
just as her mother did, she who died
alone in her sleep
at the age of ninety-two
in the fisherman's cottage she had bought herself
on the Pembrokeshire coast.

Teddy reclines on his seat
and says that he doesn't feel too well
his vision is blurry
but Polly ignores him
and turns her face towards the window
where the rain has begun to fall
again
thick drops like corn kernels
'The sun will be back'
she says
because she knows
these things
so she gathers her book, a jumper, and a few other
titbits she places in her bag, then rummages for something
ah yes, her lipstick, a golden tube which she opens carefully
and applies to her lips, bright red, too red
so she dabs the excess on a tissue and discards it
on the train floor, or perhaps her bag
I cannot see, neither can Teddy, whose eyes
are closed again, his skin has now changed colour
to a muddy green
I stand up and walk towards them both,
'Are you sure he's all right?' I ask Polly
as I see droplets of sweat
forming like a nest of ants
on his forehead

so she turns around and mutters
'Certainly, why wouldn't he be?'
but then her composure changes
a little
she says 'Teddy, we're arriving in Paris
any minute now, Teddy do you hear'
as if he were a child
but that doesn't matter
because he doesn't hear anything
anymore
his face is grey
and his lips
are tilted sideways
and his eyes are closed
'I cannot feel my face'
he whispers
and suddenly
he crumples
in front of us
unconscious
so someone pushes the alarm
and the train
shrieks to a halt
and all of us stand around Teddy and shout
'Is there a doctor on board? Is there a doctor on board?'
and a man appears quickly, Fabien
he touches Teddy's wrist
and Teddy's neck
and says in a calm voice
that we must get him to hospital
immediately
and Sophie appears at his side
as does the mother of the boy
who speaks to dragonflies

as does the man who forgot his pills
though this time he is accompanied
by a diminutive woman who says that
she is a nurse
she can help too
she whispers
to Fabien
as the Eritrean steward
arrives with the train manager
carrying a bag
of unnecessary ice
and Fabien asks us
to step away
and starts performing CPR on the man
while other staff members enter the carriage
and speak into walkie-talkies
with worried looks on their faces
'An ambulance has arrived at the station'
someone says
as the train starts again
and after a few long
minutes
Polly stands up
abruptly
and says
he's dead isn't he?
to Fabien who answers
yes I'm afraid so,
I'm terribly sorry
and she looks at him
at Teddy
why so fast
she whispers
with staggered eyes

her lips still red
she clutches
then drops
her handbag
and wraps her arms
around her shoulders
seeking a comfort
she cannot find
because there is no one
and nothing
left for her
to hate
to love
to share
so she stumbles away
towards another carriage
and we all stand
watching her disappear
watching Teddy,
stunned into silence
until someone covers
his body
with a white sheet
and the rooftops of Paris
appear against
a white sky
and the rain continues to beat
against
the window.